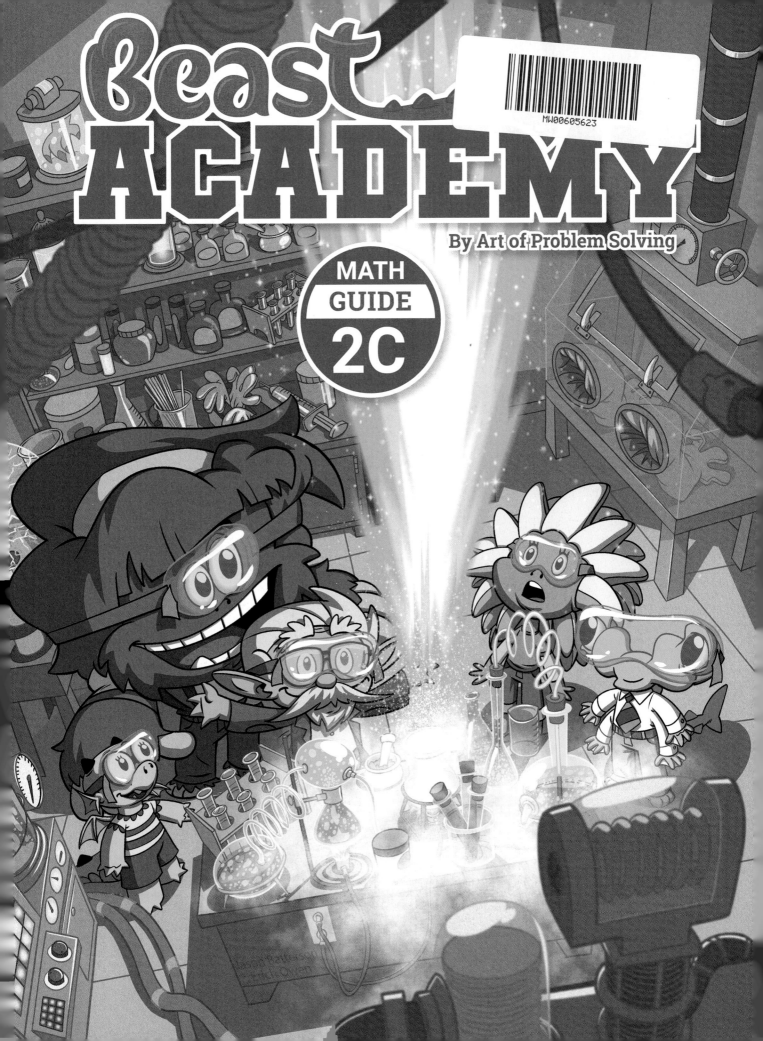

Published by: AoPS Incorporated
                     15330 Avenue of Science
                     San Diego, CA 92128
                     info@BeastAcademy.com

ISBN: 978-1-934124-34-5

Beast Academy is a registered trademark of AoPS Incorporated.

Written by Jason Batterson
Illustrated by Erich Owen
Additional Illustrations by Paul Cox
Colored by Greta Selman

Visit the Beast Academy website at BeastAcademy.com.
Visit the Art of Problem Solving website at artofproblemsolving.com.
Printed in the United States of America.
2023 Printing.

Become a Math Beast!
For additional books,
printables, and more, visit

BeastAcademy.com

This is Guide 2C in a four-book series:

Guide 2A
Chapter 1: Place Value
Chapter 2: Comparing
Chapter 3: Addition

Guide 2B
Chapter 4: Subtraction
Chapter 5: Expressions
Chapter 6: Problem Solving

Guide 2C
Chapter 7: Measurement
Chapter 8: Strategies (+&−)
Chapter 9: Odds & Evens

Guide 2D
Chapter 10: Big Numbers
Chapter 11: Algorithms (+&−)
Chapter 12: Problem Solving

Now Available!
Beast Academy Online

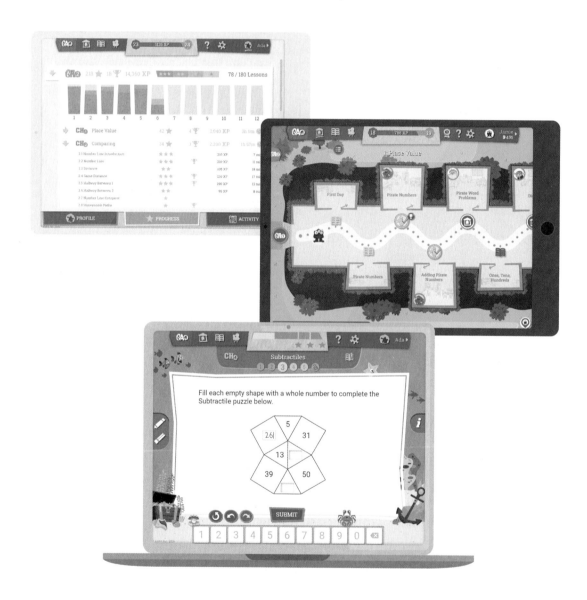

Learn more at BeastAcademy.com

Contents:

Alex
"The Executive"

Irons his socks
Only wears
them to bed

GrOgg (me!)

I can write with my feet!

(nOt as well as with my hands)

Winnie
"The Firecracker"

Testy at times

Don't be fooled
by her
cute handwriting

Lizzie
"The BOOkwOrm"

Read all 52 books
in the DragOn Diaries
series

wrOte new endings
fOr 3 Of them

← Kraken

Shop Teacher

keeps a lot of planks in his room

says they're "not for walkin'"

Fiona

was a Math Team star at Beast Academy

Now, she's the coach!

Ms. Q.

Math Teacher

knows everything

still asks a lot of questions

Professor Grok

Math Lab

Has lots of cool stuff in his lab

Has a nefarious nemesis!

calamitous clod

R&G

School caretaker(s?)

Named the mop bucket "Bessie"

wouldn't let me ride it down the hall

Bessie

Welcome to Beast Academy!

This book is called the Guide.

There is also a separate Practice book with lots of problems you can use to sharpen your skills.

The Guide is written like a comic book.

In a comic book, whatever I say shows up in these bubbles. They're called comic balloons.

Here's one!

Each character has a different balloon color. This makes it easy to tell who is talking.

My balloons are purple!

The story is told in panels.

Panels usually have a rectangular frame around them...

...like this one.

STOP SIGNS ASK QUESTIONS THAT YOU SHOULD TRY
TO ANSWER BEFORE READING ANY FURTHER.

*AN ASTERISK MAY BE USED TO TIE THE TEXT IN A COMIC BALLOON TO A GRAY BOX.

Contents: Chapter 7

See page 6 in the Practice book for a recommended reading/practice sequence for Chapter 7.

We can compare both strings to something else.

Good idea!

We can use this red string to compare the green string and the blue string.

The green string is a little shorter than the red string.

The blue string is a little longer than the red string.

So, the blue string is longer than the green one.

Great work.

We can compare two strings by comparing them both to something else.

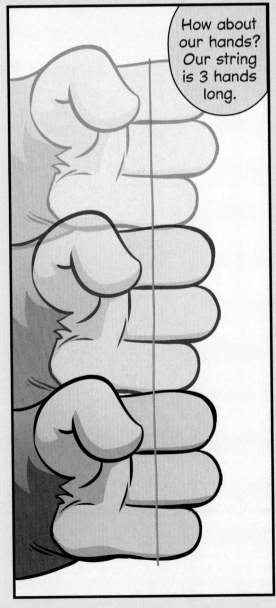

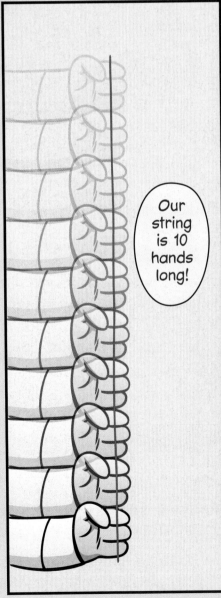

Our string is a little longer than 6 boxes.

Our string is a little shorter than 6 boxes!

So, our string is longer.

Great work!

You used the box as a *unit of measurement.*

To compare two things by measuring, we use the *same* unit of measurement.

What if you wanted to compare the lengths of your strings to the lengths of other strings...

...all over Beast Island?

How would this be possible?

We could travel from town to town with these boxes, measuring strings everywhere!

Or, we could **sell** these boxes...

...so monsters could measure their own strings!

BOXES
For Measuring STUFF

PAY HERE

2 for 1

BOXES

Or, we could just use a **ruler**.

A what?

"A **ruler** is a tool used for measuring short lengths in standard units like inches and centimeters."

That's right.

You probably have one at home, Grogg.

You'll need it for tomorrow's class.

Practice: Pages 7-11

*YOU'LL NEED A RULER, TOO! FIND ONE, AND USE IT AS YOU READ THIS SECTION!

*1 FOOT IS EQUAL TO 12 INCHES. YOU'LL LEARN MORE ABOUT FEET AND INCHES IN THE NEXT SECTION.

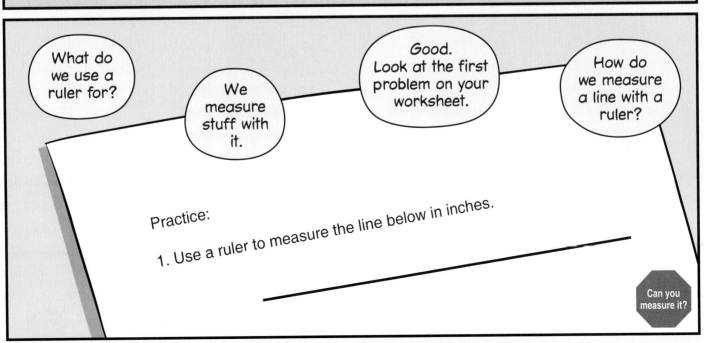

Practice:

1. Use a ruler to measure the line below in inches.

THE RULERS ABOVE ARE ACTUAL SIZE! "CM" IS SHORT FOR CENTIMETERS, AND "IN" IS SHORT FOR INCHES. YOUR RULER MIGHT LOOK SLIGHTLY DIFFERENT THAN THE ONE ABOVE.

We can start by measuring from A. From A to B is between 4 and 5 centimeters.

That's too short.

THESE RULERS ARE *NOT* ACTUAL SIZE.

From A to C is between 8 and 9 centimeters.

That's too long.

A to D and A to E are both longer than A to C.

So, they're too long, too.

Next, let's measure from B. We already measured from B to A when we measured A to B.

From B to C is between 6 and 7 centimeters.

B to D and B to E are both longer than B to C.

So, we don't need to measure those.

What's left to measure?

What's left?

25

which is LOnger? By GrOgg!

cOmpare the purple lines belOw.

which is LOnger?
1. The tOp line, Or the bOttom line?

NO way!

2. The purple line On the left Or the right?

3. The vertical (up/dOwn) line, Or the hOrizOntal (flat) line?

I DON'T believe it

4. Are these tabletOps the same size and shape?

Measure and be AMAZED!

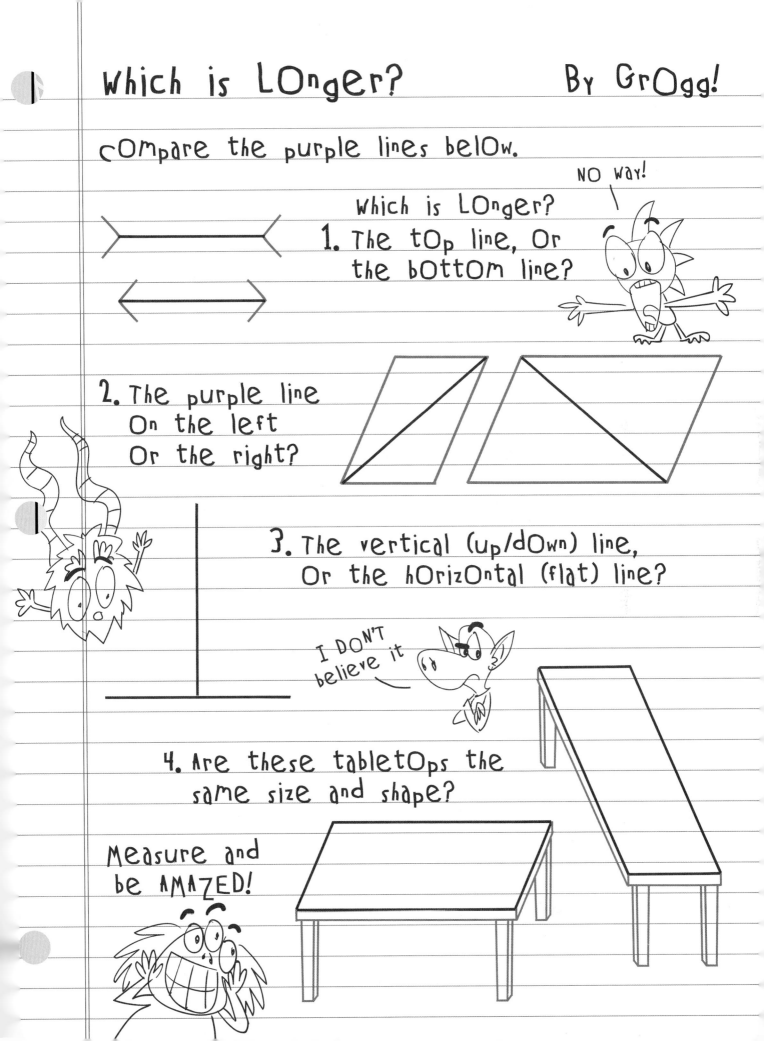

Since 1 yard is 3 feet...

...3 yards is 3+3+3=9 feet.

1 yard	1 yard	1 yard
(3 feet)	(3 feet)	(3 feet)

3+3+3=9 feet

So, there are 12 inches in 1 foot...

...and 3 feet in 1 yard...

...how many yards are in a mile?

A mile is 1,760 yards.*

Wait, **how many!?**

A mile is a *lot* of yards. 1,760!

That's 5,280 feet!

1,760 IS READ, "ONE THOUSAND, SEVEN HUNDRED SIXTY." THIS IS A BIG NUMBER THAT YOU DO NOT NEED TO REMEMBER. WE'LL LEARN MORE ABOUT BIG NUMBERS IN CHAPTER 10 OF BEAST ACADEMY 2D.

32

Practice: Pages 12-25

WOODSHOP: MIXED MEASURES

Today, you'll each be makin' your own chair usin' just two wood planks!

Since you're all different heights...

...your chairs will be different sizes.

You'll each be needin' to find your height.

For example, I be 6 feet 3 inches tall.

You used two *different* units.

Aye, when describing a monster's height, 'tis common to use feet *and* inches.

Being 6 feet 3 inches tall means my height be 6 feet plus 3 inches.

How tall is that if we just use inches?

What is Captain Kraken's height in inches?

A MEASUREMENT THAT USES TWO DIFFERENT UNITS IS CALLED A *MIXED MEASURE*.

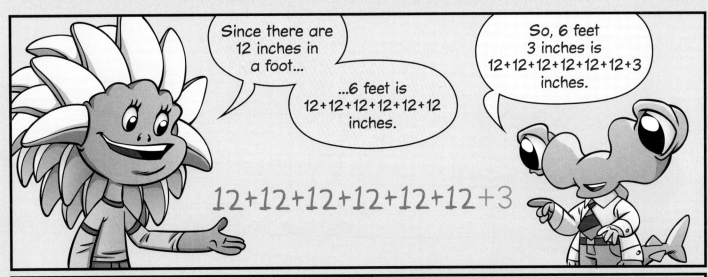

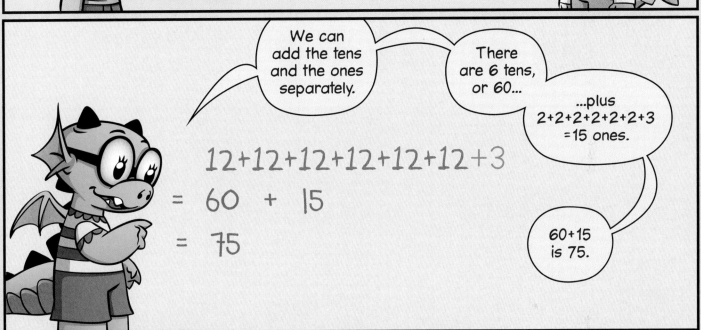

4 inches more than
1 foot 11 inches
is 1 foot and
11+4 = 15 inches.

But, that's
over 2 feet.

1 ft 11 in
+   4 in
—————
1 ft 15 in

You can regroup
12 inches to make
another foot.

That
gives us
2 feet and
15 − 12 = 3
inches.

So, your long
plank should be
2 feet 3 inches
long.

1 ft 11 in
+   4 in
~~1 ft 15 in~~
2 ft 3 in

And my short
plank should be
4 inches less than
1 foot 11 inches.

1 ft 11 in
−   4 in
—————
1 ft 7 in

That's
1 foot 7 inches.

Since I am 1 foot
taller than Lizzie,
my planks should
be 1 foot longer
than hers.

So, my planks are
3 feet 3 inches and
2 feet 7 inches.

And mine are
2 feet 10 inches...

...and
2 feet 2 inches.

2 ft 6 in
+   4 in
—————
2 ft 10 in

2 ft 6 in
−   4 in
—————
2 ft 2 in

Contents: Chapter 8

See page 36 in the Practice book for a recommended reading/practice sequence for Chapter 8.

Chapter 8: Strategies (+ & −)

$$36 - 17 + 17 =$$

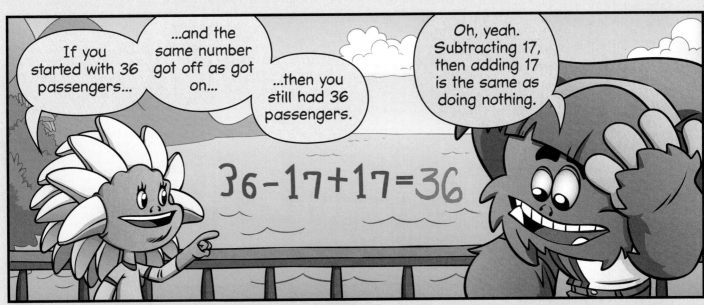

If you started with 36 passengers...

...and the same number got off as got on...

...then you still had 36 passengers.

Oh, yeah. Subtracting 17, then adding 17 is the same as doing nothing.

$$36 - 17 + 17 = 36$$

Well done. We left Hydra Harbor with 36 passengers aboard.

Alas, a huge wave washed 18 passengers into the sea.

Splash!

We quickly threw rescue nets 'n' ropes...

...'n' 19 monsters climbed aboard.

So, you had $36 - 18 + 19$ passengers after that?

Aye. How many passengers be on me ship after the rescue?

$$36 - 18 + 19 =$$

How many?

45

RECESS

Zero-Sum is a 2-player card game in which players score points by creating expressions that equal zero.

Setup

The game uses a standard deck of playing cards with the face cards (K, Q, J) removed. Aces are treated as 1's.

Black cards stand for addition. For example, a black 9 stands for +9. Red cards stand for subtraction. For example, a red 7 stands for −7. Or, find printable cards with + and − symbols at BeastAcademy.com.

Shuffle the deck and deal 4 cards face down to each player. Place the remaining cards face down in a pile called the stock. Turn four cards from the stock face up. These are the draw cards.

Play

Players take turns. On a player's turn, the goal is to create an expression that equals zero using one of the draw cards and one or more cards in their hand. The number of cards used in the expression is the number of points scored on their turn.

For example, a player can combine the red 2♦ (−2) from the draw cards above with cards from their hand to create an expression that equals zero. Several examples are given below.

$$8 \quad -6 \quad -2 \quad = 0$$

$$2 \quad -2 \quad = 0$$

$$3 \quad +5 \quad -6 \quad -2 \quad = 0$$

If a player can create an expression that equals zero, the cards used in the expression are placed in their score pile. Cards from the stock are used to replace the draw card and to fill the player's hand to 4 cards. This ends their turn.

If a player cannot create an expression that equals zero, they draw one card from the stock and end their turn.

Winning

The game ends after all of the cards in the stock have been drawn and neither player can play an expression.

The winner is the player with the most cards in their score pile.

Excellent!

Try one more. How would you evaluate this expression?

$$10 - 1 + 20 - 2 + 30 - 3 + 40$$

$$10 - 1 + 20 - 2 + 30 - 3 + 40$$
$$= \quad 9 \quad +18 \quad +27 \quad +40$$

This doesn't help much.

$$10 - 1 + 20 - 2 + 30 - 3 + 40$$
$$= 10 \quad +19 \quad +28 \quad +37$$

Neither does this.

$$10 - 1 + 20 - 2 + 30 - 3 + 40$$

I guess we can just work from left to right.

10−1 is 9...

...plus 20 is 29...

...minus 2 is 27...

I know a way to make it easier!

What would you do?

Practice: Pages 37-56

Contents: Chapter 9

See page 70 in the Practice book for a recommended reading/practice sequence for Chapter 9.

*THIS INCLUDES ZERO. SINCE O+O=O. ZERO IS AN EVEN NUMBER.

74

even+even = even

odd+odd = even

even+odd =

MATH TEAM
More Than Two

Today, we're going to explore what happens when we add more than two odds or two evens.*

*WE SOMETIMES CALL ODD NUMBERS AND EVEN NUMBERS "ODDS" AND "EVENS" FOR SHORT.

First, write four even numbers and add them.

All our sums are even.

Yep.

Will four even numbers *always* have an even sum?

$$40+18+444+2=504$$
$$2+2+2+2=8$$
$$10+20+30+40=100$$
$$2+4+8+16=30$$

Is the sum of four even numbers always even?

78

All our sums are even again.

That's true. Will four odds *always* have an even sum?

$$37 + 7 + 333 + 5 = 382$$
$$1 + 1 + 1 + 1 = 4$$
$$5 + 15 + 25 + 35 = 80$$
$$5 + 11 + 55 + 151 = 222$$

When we add four odd numbers, the first two numbers have an even sum.

Then, when we add the third odd number, we get an odd sum.

Finally, odd+odd is even.

$$odd + odd + odd + odd$$
$$even + odd + odd$$
$$odd + odd$$
$$even$$

You could also add the odd numbers in pairs, like this.

Perfect. The sum of 4 odds is always even.

Does adding more than two odds *always* give an even sum?

$$odd + odd + odd + odd$$
$$even \quad + \quad even$$
$$even$$

Does it?

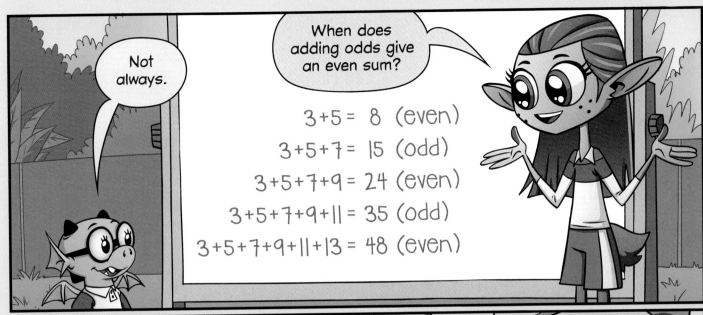

Not always.

When does adding odds give an even sum?

$3+5 = 8$ (even)
$3+5+7 = 15$ (odd)
$3+5+7+9 = 24$ (even)
$3+5+7+9+11 = 35$ (odd)
$3+5+7+9+11+13 = 48$ (even)

When you add an **odd** number of odds, the sum is odd.

But when you add an **even** number of odds, the sum is even.

Huh?

DON'T SPEND TIME TRYING TO MEMORIZE ALL OF THE RULES IN THIS CHAPTER. ONCE YOU UNDERSTAND THE BASICS OF ODDS AND EVENS, YOU CAN COME UP WITH THESE RULES AND MORE ON YOUR OWN.

odd+odd+odd+odd+odd+odd+odd+odd

even + even + even + even

even

If you add an even number of odds...

...you can add them all in pairs.

Each pair has an even sum.

Since adding even numbers always gives an even sum...

...the sum is even.

Practice: Pages 82-87

Let's see...

The first time you passed through the door, you came *into* the classroom.

And the second time you passed through the door...

...you went out.

The 3rd time, you came in...

...the 4th time, you went out...

...the 5th time, you came in...

...the 6th time, you went out...

...the 7th time, you came in--

Grogg!

Every *odd* time Captain Kraken passed through the door, he came *in* to the classroom.

Every *even* time he passed through the door, he went *out* of the classroom.

Since he's *in* the classroom now, Captain Kraken has passed though the door an *odd* number of times.

Is it possible?

93

94

95

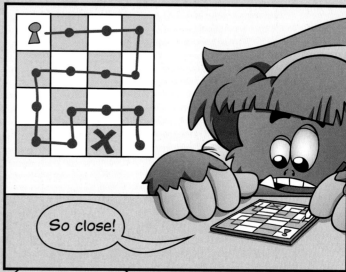

98

The last square you land on is number 16, which is even.

Since every even square is dark...

...we can only end on a **dark** square.

The bottom-right square isn't dark, so it's impossible to end on it!

Brilliant!

If you start on a light square and visit all 16 squares once, you will always end on a dark square.

I'll be right back, I just need to fetch a few supplies...

Wham!

Fwomp!

Thunk!

Professor Grok?

103

Practice: Pages 88-101

Index